5, 2, 4, 10, 12, 16
17 19

7pm Fri
7pm Sat

SERGEI RACHMANINOFF

The Liturgy of St. John Chrysostom

Edited and Translated by

ANTHONY ANTOLINI

1st Church of God 11/6

GALAXY MUSIC CORPORATION New York

Contents

Preface

The music of the Russian Orthodox Church is steeped in a tradition which is in many ways quite different from that of the Roman Catholic Church even though there are frequent similarities of text. The most obvious difference is the prohibition of any musical instruments in the services of the Russian Church, including the organ, based upon the assertion that instruments are representative of worldly things and that only unaccompanied human voices are a fitting means of singing God's praises. The historical origins of this music are rooted in the ancient Byzantine melodies of the Church which, when transplanted onto Russian soil progressed from a strict unison to a developed polyphonic style in Kiev and became known as *znamenny chant* . This later flowered into a variety of localized styles in other parts of Russia such as Moscow and Novgorod.

Compared with the five sections of the Roman Mass which have been set to music by western composers (Kyrie, Gloria, Credo, Sanctus, Agnus Dei), the Eastern Liturgy is much more extensive. Musical tradition has also prevented composers from dividing portions of the Orthodox Liturgy into separate musical movements as one sees in Bach's *Mass in B Minor*. Tradition has also placed a strong emphasis on the syllabic accentuation of the text. This coupled with the already heavily stressed syllabification of such languages as Slavonic and Russian has led to a highly distinctive style of choral music which is not well known in the west.

St. John Chrysostom (c. 347-407 A.D.) was born in Antioch and became a priest in 386. In 398 he was made patriarch of Constantinople where he quickly gained a reputation for his eloquence — his name in Greek and Russian is literally "Golden Mouth." He also alienated both the clergy and the court on numerous occasions with his outspoken denunciations of the evils of his day. In 403 he was condemned by the Empress Eudoxia and the Bishop of Alexandria in an illegal synod on false charges and without a hearing. After he was deposed, he continued to attack the immorality of the court and was exiled to Armenia. Even in exile his letters continued to influence public opinion and so he was exiled to a remote region on the Black Sea. The journey there cost him his life. In 438 his body was returned to Constantinople and Emperor Theodosius II did penance for the evils his parents had done to this righteous man. *The Liturgy of St. John Chrysostom* is named in his honor.

The Liturgy of St. John Chrysostom as a text is central to Orthodox worship and is the most frequently used. (Other services such as *The Liturgy of St. Basil the Great* or the *Liturgy of the Presanctified Gifts* are celebrated only on particular days in the liturgical year.) *The Liturgy of St. John Chrysostom* (or various sections of it) has been set by such outstanding Russian composers as Gretchaninoff, Bakhmetev, Kastalsky, Archangelsky, and Tchaikovsky. Rachmaninoff's principal model for his own setting was Tchaikovsky's, written in 1880 and well received by both the public and church authorities. Rachmaninoff's own background was not strongly religious but we do know from his *Recollections* as told to Oscar von Riesemann that he was exposed to the music of the Orthodox Church by his grandmother, Sophia Alexandrovna Boutakova when he was a boy of eleven: "We spent hours standing in the beautiful St. Petersburg churches. Being only a young greenhorn, I took less interest in God and religious worship than in the singing, which was of unrivaled beauty, especially in the cathedrals, where one frequently heard the best choirs in St. Petersburg. I usually took pains to find room underneath the gallery and never missed a single note. Thanks to my good memory, I also remembered most of what I heard. This turned into capital — literally — by sitting down at the piano when I came home, and playing all I had heard. For this performance my grandmother never failed to reward me with twenty-five kopecks." [1]

Rachmaninoff composed his *Liturgy of St. John Chrysostom* in the month of July, 1910 at his summer estate, Ivanovka, which was about 300 miles southeast of Moscow in the fertile, black-soil region of Russia. In a letter to his friend, Nikita Morozov, Rachmaninoff stated: ". . . I have been thinking about the *Liturgy* for a long time and for a long time I was striving to write it. I started work on it somehow by chance and then suddenly became fascinated with it. And then I finished it very quickly. Not for a long time . . . have I written anything with such pleasure." The score was immediately sent to Nikolai Danilin (1878-1945) who had just become senior director of the Moscow Synodal Choir. Although this choir already had the reputation as one of the greatest choral ensembles in history, Danilin complained that the work was too demanding — particularly for the basses because of so many low notes. (The same argument arose five years later with Danilin when Rachmaninoff presented him with the score of his *Vespers*. Their correspondence indicates that Danilin wrote: "Where on earth are we to find such basses? They are as rare as asparagus at Christmas.") In both instances Rachmaninoff remained optimistic and Danilin did find the basses who could do justice to the many low notes.

The work was published by Rachmaninoff's regular publisher at the time, A. Gutheil & Sons of Moscow in four separate part books (a convention that had been abandoned hundreds of years earlier in the west but which continued into the twentieth century in the choral music of the Russian Church.) The first performance was on November 25, 1910 in Moscow. Ecclesiastical authorities subsequently objected to the work's "spirit of modernism" and did not sanction it for church use. Rachmaninoff must have been disappointed with this decision because the work soon fell into relative obscurity. The following year a vastly altered version of the work was published in London by Boosey & Hawkes as an Anglican Communion Service in English with adaptations by Walter S. Vale. Other versions of a few movements of the Liturgy were published by H.W. Gray in 1914 with translations by C.W. Douglas, and by J. Fischer & Bro. in 1916 with adaptations by A.M. Henderson, but the complete work in Slavonic was not published again after the original Russian edition of 1910. Thus, the present edition is the first complete authentic version available since that time, as well as the first edition in a modern choral score format.

The first American concert performance of a portion of Rachmaninoff's *Liturgy* was given in New York on January 24, 1914 by the male choir of the Russian Cathedral of St. Nicholas at Symphony Hall under the direction of Ivan Gorokhov. The program was repeated a week later at Harvard University and featured six movements of Rachmaninoff's *Liturgy* and six of Tchaikovsky's. A review in the Boston newspaper said: "Rachmaninoff excelled Tchaikovsky in fertility of technical means and in range and significance of invention, and with linear music of interwoven strands . . . the music . . . moved always in plastic line or in vividly superimposed phrases under Mr. Gorokhov's masterful hand. . ."

Locating copies of the original 1910 Gutheil edition of Rachmaninoff's *Liturgy* proved to be a challenge. After months of searching, a complete set of the original part books was found at St. Tikhon's Monastery in South Canaan, Pennsylvania. The Reverend Theodore Heckmann, Director of Music at St. Tikhon's, very generously provided photocopies of all four part books. A microfilm of the full conductor's score was found in the United States Library of Congress' Rachmaninoff Archive with the generous assistance of Wayne Shirley. However, the microfilm was old and damaged in many places, rendering the notes illegible. Whenever such problems arose the part books provided indisputable evidence of the correct notes or rhythms.

The piano reductions, which should be used for rehearsal only, appear in the original full score and are the composer's own work (occasionally showing his penchant for writing piano music rather than an exact reduction of the choral parts.) The present edition is based entirely upon the 1910 Gutheil edition.

In performance of this work the editor has found that the potential problems posed by the low tessitura of the bass parts (often compounded by flatting in all parts) may be remedied by raising the pitch of all movements a half step.

The present edition is intended primarily for concert performance. However, it may be adapted for liturgical use as well because all the choral responses composed by Rachmaninoff have been included. It is important to note that Rachmaninoff composed the choral responses but not the chants of the clergy. The chants included in Appendix I are suggestions based upon common practice but were not included in the original 1910 edition. The editor has found that the inclusion of some chant in concert performance is effective not only as a means of giving pitch to the chorus but also in lending an important element of atmosphere of what the work would sound like if it were heard in a liturgical setting.

The subject of how much chant to include in the concert performance of an Orthodox Liturgy is an open question. Vladimir Morosan, in his excellent book, *Choral Performance in Pre-Revolutionary Russia* states:

> Given the solid precedent for concert performance of liturgical works established in Russia before the Revolution, the conductor who wishes to perform these works in concert or on a recording must decide whether the usual ekphonesis of the clergy should be included to create a more complete musical-liturgical entity. . . . Although such composers as Tchaikovsky, Grechaninov, and Rachmaninoff apparently composed with liturgical considerations in mind when they set the various litanies and responses for the chorus, their highly artistic and subjective interpretations of the hymns, and the purely musical features of their compositions, such as choral sonority and intense musical expression, are often best perceived in a concert performance unburdened by the liturgical minutiae. In addition, there is the question of stylistic unity: if a composer did not compose all the elements of a given service (as Rachmaninoff did not . . .), these elements must be supplied from the common chant repertoire or from the works of some other composer. If these choices are not made wisely, the full musical impact of a masterpiece such as Rachmaninoff's may be lost, aside from the fact that one hour of Rachmaninoff's music becomes stretched over two-and-a-half or three hours. . . . Unfortunately, no composers have left composed settings of [the] ekphonetic exclamations [the clergy's sentences], and the few manuals of ekphonesis published in Russia are not only scarce, but present an extremely simplified, decadent tradition of ekphonesis.[2]

— **Anthony Antolini, December 1987**

---

[1]. *Rachmaninov's Recollections* Told to Oskar von Riesemann, New York, Macmillan, 1934, pp. 33-34.
[2]. Morosan, Vladimir, *Choral Performance in Pre-Revolutionary Russia*, UMI Research Press, 1986, pp. 302-303.

No. 1   Velikaya Ekteniya[1.]
The Great Litany

Edition and English
Translation by
Anthony Antolini

Sergei Rachmaninoff Op. 31

[1.] Chant to precede this movement will be found in Appendix I.
[2.] Note: Throughout the work, the words *Gospodi pomiluuy* have been translated as "Lord, have mercy on us." It is also possible to insert the Greek words *Kyrie eleison* which have the same meaning and the same number of syllables.   —A.A.

2

4

No. 2 Blagoslovi, dushe moya, Gospoda[1]

Bless Thou the Lord, O My Soul (The First Antiphon)

Psalm 103:1-6

1. Chant to be sung before the final *Amin* of this movement will be found in Appendix I.
2. Although not specified by Rachmaninoff, a soloist or group of solo voices is effective.
   Other similar points are marked with the word "Solo" in brackets. — A.A.

6

12

3. Chant, if used, should be sung here. See Appendix I. If chant is not used, the *Amin* may be omitted.

No. 3 Slava Otsu i Yedinorodnï[1.]

Gloria and Only Begotten Son (The Second Antiphon)

1. Chant to be sung before the final *Amin* of this movement will be found in Appendix I.

14

16

18

Moderato

2. Chant, if used, should be sung at these rests. See Appendix I.
3. Use these 2 alternative measures only if movement 4 is to be transposed a tone higher.

No. 4   Vo tsarstvii Tvoyem
The Beatitudes (The Third Antiphon)

Matthew 5:3-12

poco più mosso

24

Poco più mosso e sostenuto (calmly)

poco più mosso

poco a poco ritardando

28

No. 5   Priiditye, poklonimsya[1]
Come, Let Us Worship

1. Chant to precede this movement will be found in Appendix I.

32

No. 6 Gospodi, spasi blagochestivïya i Svyatï Bozhe[1]
Lord, to Thee and O Thou Holy (Trisagion)

[1] Chant to precede this movement will be found in Appendix I.

36

38

No. 7 Sugubaya i Posleduyushchiya Ekteniya[1,5]
Twofold and Subsequent Litany

1. Chant to precede this movement is given in Appendix I.
2. See Appendix I for instructions on the use of chant.
3. As noted previously, "Kyrie eleison" may also be substituted for "Gospodi pomiluuy".
4. Throughout the following litany these two notes can be held at the fermatas while the deacon chants on the note D.
   (To be observed if sung for liturgical use.)
5. See Appendix III.

40

vyelitsey milosti Tvoyéy, mólim Ti sya, uslïshi i pomíluuy. Yéshche mólimsya o presvyatyéshem mitropolítye

náshem, o brátiyakh náshikh, o svyashchénnitsekh, svyashchénnomonasyekh i fsyem vo Khrístye bratsvye náshem.

Yéshche mólimsya o fsyem khristolyubívom vóinstvye. Yésche mólimsya o blazhénnïkh i prisnopámyatnïkh

sozdátyelyekh svyatágo khráma syegó, i o fsyekh pryézhdye pochívshikh otsékh i brátiyakh, zdye blagochéstno

42

44

truzháyushchikhsya, poyúshchikh i pryedstoyáschchikh lyúdyekh, ozhidáyuschchikh ot Tebyé vyelíkiya i bogátïya mílosti.

po - mi - luuy!
have mer - cy.

po - mi - luuy!
have mer - cy.

A - min.
A - men.

Go - spo - di,
Ho - ly Lord,

Go - spo - di,
Ho - ly Lord,

A - min.
A - men.

po - mi - luuy!
have mer - cy.

po - mi - luuy!
have mer - cy.

A - min.
A - men.

Go - spo - di,
Ho - ly Lord,

Go - spo - di,
Ho - ly Lord,

A - min.
A - men.

po - mi - luuy!
have mer - cy.

po - mi - luuy!
have mer - cy.

A - min.
A - men.

Note: In concert performance, it is recommended that the movement end here. For liturgical use, additional music is given in Appendix III.

No. 8 Izhe Kheruvimï
Cherubic Hymn

48

50

51

53

rallentando e diminuendo (even slower and softer)

No. 9 Prosityel'naya Ekteniya [1]
Litany of Supplication

Andantino (Rather slow)

1. Chant to precede this movement is given in Appendix I.
2. As noted previously, "Kyrie eleison" may also be substituted for "Gospodi, pomiluuy".

56

No. 10   Vyeruyu[1.]

Nicene Creed

Allegretto e tranquillo (Fairly fast, peacefully, unhurried)

1. Chant to precede this movement is given in Appendix I.

58

60

4 Sopranos 4 Altos unison
1 Tenor (sounding actual pitch)

Tempo I

Poco più mosso e marcato
Very rhythmically; with a short sound

Tempo I. Molto tranquillo e dolce (Very peaceful and warm)

poco meno (a little slower)

2. In English performance the Bass II cutoff consonant should be de-emphasized here.
3. In English performance a pause should be observed before beginning this phrase.

molto

No. 11 Milost' mira[1].
Grace of Peace

1. Chant to precede this movement is given in Appendix I.

72

2. In concert performance it is suggested to omit this section and go directly to the Adagio in $\frac{6}{4}$.

74

No. 12 Tebye poyem [1]

To Thee We Sing

Adagio, molto piano (Very slow. Barely audible. Almost without dynamic shadings.)

1. Chant to precede this movement is given in Appendix I.

* From here to the end of No. 12, the choir may sing with closed mouths.

ritardando

No. 13   Dostoyno yest'[1.]

We Laud Thy Name (Hymn to the Virgin Mary)

1. Chant to precede this movement is given in Appendix I.

84

2. It is suggested that the movement end here in concert performance. *A.A.*

In the same tempo

No. 14 Otche nash
The Lord's Prayer

94

96

98

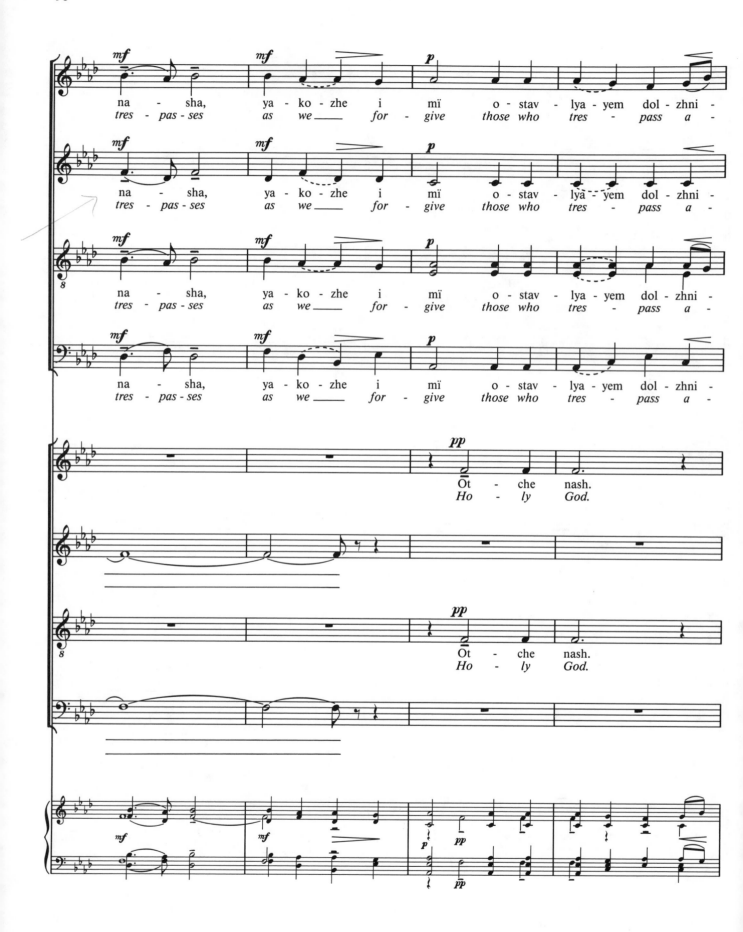

100

No. 15 I dukhovi Tvoyemu i Yedin Svyat[1.]

We Pray to Thee and Thou Art Holy

1. Chant to precede this section is given in Appendix I.
2. In concert performance, it is recommended that the movement start at the *Allegretto* and *attacca* No. 16.

spod',_____ I - i - sus Khri - stos,_____ vo sla - vu Bo - ga Ot - sa. A - min.
Lord,_____ O Thou Je - sus Christ,_____ in the glo - ry of God, A - men.

spod',_____ I - i - sus Khri - stos,_____ vo sla - vu Bo - ga Ot - sa. A - min.
Lord,_____ O Thou Je - sus Christ,_____ in the glo - ry of God, A - men.

spod',_____ I - i - sus Khri - stos,_____ vo sla - vu Bo - ga Ot - sa. A - min.
Lord,_____ O Thou Je - sus Christ,_____ in the glo - ry of God, A - men.

spod',_____ I - i - sus Khri - stos,_____ vo sla - vu Bo - ga Ot - sa. A - min.
Lord,_____ O Thou Je - sus Christ,_____ in the glo - ry of God, A - men.

attacca

No. 16 Khvalitye Gospoda s nyebyes

O Praise the Lord from the Heavens

106

ritard. e diminuendo

markedly slower

108

110

No. 17 Blagoslovyen gryadï i Vidyekhom svyet istinnï [1]

Blessed Is He Who Comes and We Have Seen the Light of Truth

[1]. Chant to precede this movement will be found in Appendix I.

112

dyel' — nyey Tro - i - tse po - kla - nya — yem-sya — ed
praise — the Tri - ni - ty un - di - vid — ed

Ta bo nas spa - sla yest,' — spa - sla yest'. A - min.
Thou, O God hast saved us, — hast saved us. A - men.

1. Chant to be inserted here is given in Appendix I.

pg 123

No. 18 Da ispolnyatsya usta nasha

May Our Mouths Be Filled with Thy Glory

116

118

120

dyen' po - u - cha - ti - sya prav - dye
day we may praise Thy name and Thy

dyen' po - u - cha - ti - sya prav - dye
day we may praise Thy name and Thy

dyen' po - u - cha - ti - sya prav - dye
day we may praise Thy name and Thy

dyen' po - u - cha - ti - sya prav - dye
day we may praise Thy name and Thy

Tvo - yey. Al - li - lu - ya Al - li - lu - ya,
glo - ry. Al - le - lu - ia Al - le - lu - ia,

Tvo - yey. Al - li - lu - ya Al - li - lu - ya,
glo - ry. Al - le - lu - ia Al - le - lu - ia,

Tvo - yey. Al - li - lu - ya, Al - li -
glo - ry. Al - le - lu - ia, Al - le -

Tvo - yey. Al - li - lu - ya Al - li -
glo - ry. Al - le - lu - ia Al - le -

1. Chant to be inserted here will be found in Appendix I
2. Chant to be inserted here will be found in Appendix I

No. 19 Budi imya Gospodnye [1.]

May the Name of the Lord Be Blessed

1. Chant to precede this movement is given in Appendix I.

124

126

127

No. 20 Slava Otsu i Blagochestivyeyshago
Praise to the Father

130

*The Slavonic text is translated as "Orthodox Christians," a standard form in all Orthodox services — *A.A.*

Appendix I

Throughout, the chants notated in bass clef are sung by the DEACON (bass) and those notated in the tenor clef are sung by the PRIEST (tenor).

To be sung before No. 1 Velikaya Ekteniaya.

Bla - go - slo - ví, vla - dï - ko.

Blagoslovyénno tsárstvo, Ot - sa i sïna, i Svyatágo Dú - kha, nïnye i prísno, i vo vye - ki vye - kof.

Before No. 2 Blagoslovi, dushe moya, Gospoda, no chant is sung. At the end of No. 2 on page 12, before the final Amin, the following chant is sung.

Yáko Tvoyá dyerzháva, i Tvoyé yest' tsarstvo, i sí - la i slá - va, Ot - sá, i Sïna, i Svyatágo Dú - kha

nï - nye i prí - sno i vo vye - ki vye - kof.

No. 3 follows immediately.

At the end of No. 3 Slava Otsu i Yedinorodni, bottom of page 19, the following chant is to be sung before the first Amin. The second Amin is used only if the next movement is to be transposed a tone higher than written.

Yáko blák i chelovyekolyúbyets Bok ye - sí, i Te - byé slá - vu vosïláyem, Ot - su, i Sïnu, i Svyatómu Du - khu,

nïnye i pri - sno i vo vye - ki vye - kof.

To be sung before No. 5 Priiditye, poklonimsya.

Prye - mu - drost', pro - sti.

To be sung before No. 6 Gospodi, spasi blagochestiviya.

Góspodi, spasí bla - go - che - stí - vï - ya.

To be sung before No. 7 Sugabaya i poslyeduyushchiya Ekteniya.

The chant written above the chorus parts in No. 7 is to be sung simultaneously with the choral parts, but not synchronized in any particular way with them. At the end of the movement, the choir simply waits for the DEACON to finish the chant before singing the final Amin.

Rtsem fsi ot fsyéya dushí, i ot fsyevó pomïshlyéniya na - she - go rtsem.

Before No. 8 Izhe Kheruvimi, no chant is sung.

To be sung before No. 9 Prositel'naya Ekteniya.

Ispólnim molítvu na - shu Góspodye - vi.

To be sung before No. 10 Vyeruyu.

Dvyé - ri, dvyé - ri, prye - mú - dro - sti - yu von - myem.

To be sung before **No. 11 Milost' mira.**

Stányem dóbrye, stányem so strákhom, vónmyem: svyatóye voznoshéniyev mi - rye pri - no - si - ti.

To be sung before **No. 12 Tebye poyem.**

Tvoyá ot Tvoyíkh, Tebyé prinosyáshche o fsyekh i za fsya.

To be sung before **No. 13 Dostoyno yest'.**

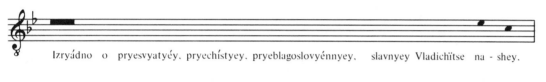

Izryádno o pryesvyatyéy, pryechístyey, pryeblagoslovyénnyey, slavnyey Vladichïtse na - shey.

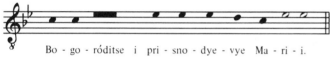

Bo - go - róditse i pri - sno - dye - vye Ma - ri - i.

Before No. 14 Otche nash, no chant is sung.

To be sung before the Allegretto, page 103, **No. 15 Yedin Svyat.** The slow **I dukhovi Tvoyemu** section may be omitted in concert performance.

Von - myem.

Svya - tá - ya svya - tïm.

No. 16 follows immediately.

To be sung before **No. 17 Blagoslovyen gryad ï.**

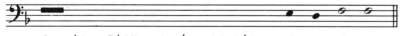

So strákhom Bózhiim, i vyéroyu i lyubóviyu, pri - stu - pi - tye.

134

To be sung at the end of No. 17, page 113, before the final Amin.

Fsyegda, nïnye i pri - sno, i vo vyé - ki vye - kof.

No. 18 follows immediately.

To be sung at the end of **No. 18 Da ispolnyatsya usta nasha** before the final Gospodi pomiluuy at the bottom system of page 122.

Gos - spo - du po - mo - lim - sya.

The chorus responds with the final Gospodi pomiluuy. Then the following chant is sung before the final Amin.

Ya - ko fsyá - koye dayániye blágo, i fsyak dar sovyershén sÏÏ - she yest'.

skhodyáy, ot Tebyé Ot - sa svyé - tof: i Tebye slávu, i blagodaryénie, i po - klo - nye - ni - ye

vosïláyem, Otsu, i SÏnu, i Svyatómu Dúkhu, nï - nye i pri - sno, i vye - ki vye - kof.

To be sung before **No. 19 Budi imya Gospodnye.**

Búdi ímya Gospódnye blagoslovyénno ot nïnye i do vye - ka.

Before No. 20 Slava Otsu i Blagochestivyeyshago, no chant is sung.

Appendix II

Pronunciation Guide
for the Slavonic Transliteration

Slavonic, the language of the Liturgy, dates from the latter part of the seventeenth century, and should not be pronounced like modern Russian. In general, Slavonic should be pronounced phonetically as noted below.

Vowels

No Slavonic vowel (or consonant) sound is exactly like the equivalent English sound presented below. Unlike modern Russian, Slavonic vowels are always pronounced with full value (never reduced in value on unaccented syllables). Slavonic vowels tend to be purer than the equivalent English vowel sounds, i.e, they lack the English tendency toward diphthongs.

Character	Pronunciation	Slavonic
[a]	a as in father	slava
[o]	deep, dark aw as in the British awful, thought	Bozhe
[u]	as oo in moot	Dukhu
[e]	eh as in bed	nashego
[i]	i as in machine	spasi
[y]	(initial position) y as in yes	yedin
[y]	(following vowels) y as in toy	dostoyno
[ï]	No English equivalent, pronounce oo with lips drawn back in the position for ee. The resulting sound is similar to the i sound in sit. This sound is identical to the modern Russian vowel ЬІ.	

A double vowel is articulated separately when there are separate note values for each vowel.

Marii

Consonants

All consonants as in English, noting the following:

Character	Pronunciation	Slavonic
[g]	with slightly guttural sound, never pronounced like the soft English g in larger	dolgi
[ts]	ts as in blots	Tsarya
[r]	trilled as in Italian	radi
[kh]	ch as in the German Bach, ach	kheruvimi
[ch]	as in cheese	chelovyek
[sh]	as in sharp	dushe
[shch]	shch as in fresh cheese	sidyashche
[zh]	s as in pleasure, treasure	blazheni

A double consonant is held very slightly longer than a single consonant

rozhdyenna

Occasionally, a single syllable word in Slavonic will contain several consonants without intervening vowels. Such words should be pronounced as monosyllables since they appear on single notes on the music.

pyesn'
(not pyesen')

This mark has no sound value and does not occur in English. It makes the preceding consonant less distinct. This mark is only shown in the transcription when the pronunciation is clearly altered. It corresponds with the modern Russian ъ.

milost'

Diphthongs

Diphthongs occur with the letter y, as in:

tayno	diphthong syllable pronounced tie
zhityeyskoye	diphthong syllable pronounced like the Biblical yea
dostoyno	diphthong syllable pronounced toy
pomiluuy	diphthong syllable pronounced luuy

Specific Words and Syllables

Gospodi	This word, meaning Lord, should be pronounced with a slightly guttural sound, though not as guttural as the German ch in Bach, Buch, ach.
pomiluuy	This word, meaning have mercy, is deliberately transcribed with the double u to remind the singer that the u is to be held out as long as possible, with only a slight y off-glide at the end of the word.
Gospodi, radi, etc.	The final di should be pronounced with the d as soft as possible with a slight y sound as in 'had ye known,' 'did ye see.'

Accented Syllables

Slavonic syllable accentuation differs markedly from English in that it features one very heavily accented syllable per word regardless of the length of the word. This has a strong influence on the performance of choral music in Slavonic, since the word accents, marked in the score with the symbol –, must have a brief but powerful accent with a quick return to the marked dynamics (not a crescendo). Marcato signs, using the symbol >, should be sung even more heavily accented than those with the symbol –.

Appendix III

The following section is to be used if a litany for the departed is offered. If used, it is to be added to the end of No. 7 Sugubaya; Posleduyushchiya Ekteniya.

138

Bózhiikh, i o yézhe prostítisya im fsyákomu pryegryeshéniyu, vól'nomu zhe i nyevól'nomu. Yáko da Gospod' Bog uchinít dúshï ikh, idyézhe

právyednii uspokoyáyutsya. Mílosti Bózhiya, tsárstviya, nyebyésnago, i ostavlyéniya gryekhóf ikh, u Khristá byessmyértnago, Tsaryá i Bóga náshego prósim.

At this point, the chant procedure changes to the usual versicle and response style rather than the simultaneous pedal note of the BASS (DEACON) against the choral texture. The BASS chants the verse at the points marked with arrows. When he has finished, the choir responds with the music given below. The reciting tone of the BASS is lowered a whole step to the note C.

The actual prayers change as the occasion demands, and so are not included here. Some may be found in the Russian Orthodox Prayerbook.

140

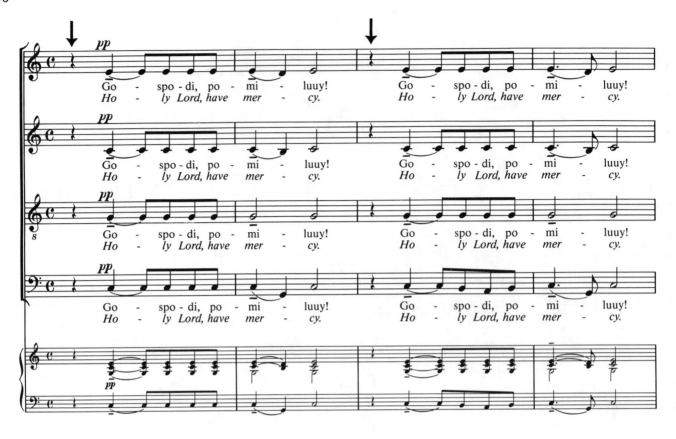

142

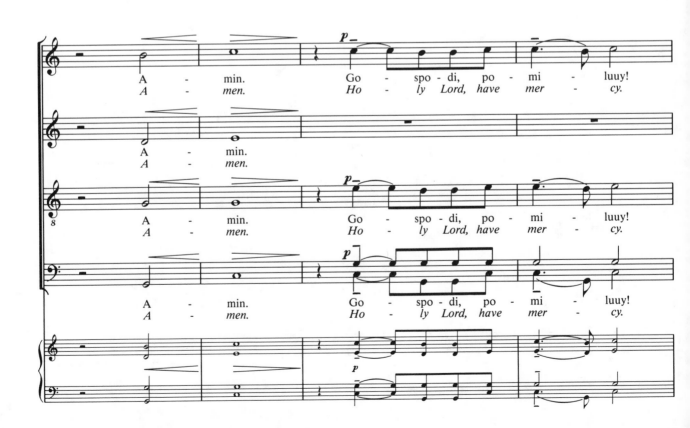

Appendix IV

Editorial Method: English Version

As much as possible, the note values of the original Slavonic have been retained. No pitches have been altered. When added rhythmic values have been necessary for the English text, the added notes are shown in cue size notes in the voice parts but not in the piano reduction. Dotted slurs are used to indicate English melismas.

Throughout the work the editor has made every effort to have the English text reflect the meaning of the original Slavonic words, preferably in the same musical phrases. Exceptions to this rule are in the brief choral responses at the beginnings and endings of movements, where alteration of the meaning of the text was necessary because the original words are responses to the clergy's prayers in the liturgy.

Where feasible, the English vowels and consonants correspond as closely as possible to the original Slavonic vowels and consonants.

Because preservation of Rachmaninoff's original notes and rhythms was given highest priority, the English text frequently differs from established liturgical texts such as those in The Book of Common Prayer, or the translation of The Liturgy of St. John Chrysostom as published by the Orthodox Church in America for liturgical use.

Acknowledgements

The editor would like to acknowledge the following people and organizations who provided generous assistance in the preparation of this edition: Members of the Cabrillo College Chorus, Jennifer Schuette, Myron J. Roberts, The Cabrillo College Foundation, Keith and Elinor Shaffer, Cabrillo College Performing Arts Division, Wayne Shirley, The United States Library of Congress, The Reverend Theodore Heckman, St. Tikhon's Monastery, Jacqueline Ryan, Nicholas Brill, The Reverend Ambrosius Pogodin, Galia Penwarden, Pamela Decker, Sharon Thoms, Stephan Beskid.